PLANTS OF ICELAND

Traditional uses and folklore

Guðrún Bjarnadóttir

&

Jóhann Óli Hilmarsson

2018

Plants of Iceland. Traditional uses and folklore
Text © Guðrún Bjarnadóttir (hespa@hespa.is)
Photographs © Jóhann Óli Hilmarsson (johannoli@johannoli.com)
Illustrations © Bjarni Guðmundsson
Design and layout: Rósa Björk / errbe.com
Proof reading: Jóhanna Snorradóttir and Erna Erlingsdóttir
Translation: Edward Rickson
Printing: Prentmiðlun / Latvia

Publishers: Guðrún Bjarnadóttir and Jóhann Óli Hilmarsson
All rights reserved
Borgarfjörður 2018
Second edition, minor changes

ISBN 978-9935-24-363-8

TABLE OF CONTENT

Mountain Avens	11	Downy Birch	73
Common Butterwort	15	White Clover	77
Round-leaved Sundew	17	Dandelion	81
Garden Angelica	19	Herb-Paris	85
Iceland Moss	23	Wild Thyme	87
Berries	29	Yarrow	91
Crowberry	31	Sea Thrift	95
Bog Bilberry & Common Bilberry	35	Moss Campion	97
		Roseroot	99
Stone Bramble	39	Marshmarigold	101
Common Juniper	41	Hairy Lady's-mantle	103
Bearberry	45	Harebell	105
Heather	49	Field Gentian	107
Lichen	51	Common Moonwort	109
Wood Cranesbill	55	Nootka Lupin	111
Madder	57	Alpine Gentian	113
Bogbean	61	Meadowsweet	115
Northern Dock	63	Orchid family Orchidaceae	119
Common Sorrel	67	Sea Mayweed	123
Common Cottongrass & Scheuchzer's Cottongrass	69	Lyme-grass	125
		Bibliography	126

FOREWORD

People have been gathering and making use of plants in Iceland ever since Settlement. However, precisely what methods and what species were used in those early days will never be known with any certainty. Iceland is believed to have been settled continuously since the 9th century but written records did not begin in earnest until the 12th century. History was probably written by the men, while the women, children and old folk gathered herbs, meaning that their story was less likely to be told. Men helped out when plants were gathered on a larger scale, such as with angelica, lichen and seaweed, but they left the smaller tasks to others. The way in which plants have been traditionally used is undoubtedly linked in some way to the countries of our ancestors, i.e. Norway, Britain and Ireland. A high proportion of our female line of ancestry is thought to have come from the British Isles and our traditions of collecting and using plants could have their roots there.

Iceland has relatively few species of plants compared with many other countries. While Norway has around 1,300 species of vascular plants and the British Isles boasts 4,000-6,000 species, a mere 500 are found in Iceland. The opportunities for using plants are therefore far more limited than in our neighbouring countries. The fact that Iceland is an island also makes it more difficult for new plants to colonize.

Plants have been used as animal fodder and for human consumption, for making tea, as medicine, dye, building material, for sewing, as padding for packhorses, as turf underlay, for firewood, to provide a fragrant aroma inside houses, just to name a few examples. Folklore and the traditional

use of plants have long been entwined. There was generally little under-
standing of the chemical properties of herbs so people often needed to
seek explanations in folklore or magic. The healing properties of plants
were even linked to their appearance, e.g. lichens, which resembled ears,
were said to cure earache, and the common orange lichen was used
as a cure for jaundice. A broth made from the leaves of sundew was
supposed to get rid of freckles as the leaf appears as if it is freckled.

Guðrún Bjarnadóttir   *Jóhann Óli Hilmarsson*

This book will range widely through Icelandic nature and explore
the traditional use of some plants and the folklore associated with them.

Guðrún Bjarnadóttir teaches botany and plant identification at the
Agricultural University of Iceland. She also runs the plant dye workshop
Hespuhúsið in Borgarfjörður in western Iceland. This book expands on
her MSc thesis: The traditional use of plants in Iceland - a comparison
with Norway and neighbouring countries. The thesis examined the tradi-

tional use of plants in Iceland since Settlement. This book also introduces folklore and stories associated with plants which were not included in the thesis.

Jóhann Óli Hilmarsson is one of Iceland's leading bird photographers and has photographed all aspects of the natural world in Iceland. This books contains a collection of his photographs of plants. His book The Icelandic Bird Guide has sold almost 50,000 copies in three languages. He has also written and had his photographs published in several other books, and has contributed many articles to magazines, newspapers and books. He has held numerous courses, lectures and exhibitions and his photographs have appeared throughout the world, including on stamps and bank notes. He is president of BirdLife Iceland.

Bjarni Guðmundsson provided the illustrations for the book. He is well known for his books on the history of agriculture. After studying agricultural sciences at Hvanneyri in Iceland and the Norwegian University for Life Sciences he conducted research and taught at the Agricultural University of Iceland at Hvanneyri. He was also director of the Agricultural Museum of Iceland for many years. In his spare time Bjarni enjoys music and drawing.

The botanical information on the species in the book comes from The Flowering Plants and Ferns of Iceland by Hörður Kristinsson. Hörður is one of Iceland's leading botanists and he has written more than 150 papers on botany and natural history. The Flowering Plants and Ferns of Iceland has been the book of choice for identifying plants in Iceland for more than 30 years.

MOUNTAIN AVENS

Icelandic: Holtasóley
Scientific: Dryas octopetala
Habitat: Common throughout Iceland in gravelly hills and dry heathland.

In 2004 the mountain avens was voted Iceland's national flower. Mountain avens grows throughout the country and, as its scientific name suggests, its flowers have eight petals. In fruit, an attractive woolly cluster forms around the head which gives the Icelandic nicknames *hárbrúða* or "hairy doll" and *hármey* or "hairy maiden." The fine leaves are referred to as "ptarmigan leaves" since they are an important source of food for the Rock Ptarmigan (*Lagopus muta*). The leaves were used by themselves or mixed with other types of leaf to make a healthy broth. A broth made of wild thyme (*Thymus praecox subsp. arcticus*) and "ptarmigan leaves" was a common remedy for colds and the flu. The genus name Dryas means "like an oak" and this refers to the leaves which are shaped like oak leaves. Linnaeus was also apparently reminded of the dryads or wood nymphs of classical mythology.

Among the reasons that the mountain avens was chosen to be Iceland's national flower was that it was easy to draw the flower and that it was so common throughout Iceland that everyone was familiar with it. However, mountain avens flowers in early June and has already adopted its woolly head when most city dwellers go on their summer holidays and therefore it may not be quite as well known by people as originally thought.

11

Hárbrúða "hairy doll"

The Icelandic vernacular name þjófarót, meaning "thief root," comes from the old belief that the root of the mountain avens could attract silver and there is a folk tale associated with this belief.

"Thief root is a plant with a whitish flower. It is said to grow wherever thieves have been hanged and it sprouts from the dying thief's spittle. Other people say it sprouts from the thief's grave mound. The root of this plant is many-branched. When the thief root is dug up you have to dig around all of those roots without cutting any of them, except the taproot which goes into the ground, this must be severed. However, any creature which hears the snap when the taproot cut is immediately struck stone dead. That's why people digging out the roots bind felt around their ears. But in order to make doubly sure they do not hear a thing, they take the precaution of putting a twine around the root and tying the other end to a dog they have brought along. When everything is ready, they leave the dig site and when they have come a safe distance they call to the dog. The root is severed as the dog runs towards the people and the dog drops down dead as soon as it hears the snap of the taproot. The root is then collected and carefully stored. This plant attracts buried silver from the ground like the seashore mouse of legend draws money from the sea. But first one has to steal the money of a destitute widow after the opening prayer at one of the three major church holy days during the year. But the root only attracts the same kind of coins that were stolen from it in the first place, if it was a shilling piece, it will only attract shilling pieces. I have never heard of problems keeping or getting rid of this root; it can be thrown away anytime and anywhere for whatever reason."

Jón Árnason, 1956, Volume 4, p. 22

COMMON BUTTERWORT

Icelandic: Lyfjagras
Scientific: Pinguicula vulgaris
Habitat: Heathland, pastures, moist banks and open ground. Common.

The common butterwort takes its name from the ability of its leaves to coagulate milk and it was traditionally used to make the Icelandic dairy product *skyr*. This use is also reflected in the Icelandic name *lyfjagras*. In the old days rennet from a calf's stomach was also used for the same purpose because it contains similar chemicals to the leaves of the common butterwort which cause milk to curdle. If cows graze on common butterwort in a meadow the milk tends to curdle and this was attributed to supernatural causes, even though it was undoubtedly a question of diet. The plant was also used to treat inflammation of the udders in cows. Mashed leaves were placed up against the udder and sulphurous vapours were wafted over the affected area. The herb was also boiled with tallow and applied to the udder.

The common butterwort feeds on proteins it extracts from flies and other invertebrates. The plant lures invertebrates to its leaves which are covered in a slime or digestive enzyme which is secreted from glands on its surface. The invertebrate prey become stuck to the leaves which curl over and digest the animal and the nutrients are absorbed into the roots. It is one of three carnivorous species in Iceland, the other two being the lesser bladderwort (*Urticularia minor*) and the round-leaved sundew (*Drosera rotundifolia*).

ROUND-LEAVED SUNDEW

Icelandic: Sóldögg
Scientific: Drosera rotundifolia
Habitat: Mossy hummocks in acid bogs, boggy edges below hillsides. Rather rare.

The round-leaved sundew feeds on insects which it lures to its leaves. Insects become stuck on the leaves which are covered with long glandular hairs secreting digestive enzymes. The hairs wrap around the insects and dissolve them. The glandular hairs bear a resemblance to freckles and this is perhaps why it was thought the enzymes could be used to get rid of freckles. But why do children get freckles in the first place? According to folk belief it was because the mother had eaten Ptarmigan eggs during pregnancy. In the 17th century the dew-like enzymes from the plant were added to a glass of schnapps and this was thought to have miraculous healing powers and kept the doctor away. The drops were called *Aqua vita roris solis,* which means "water of life sun dew" and it was thought to be able to get rid of warts, corns and freckles.

GARDEN ANGELICA

Icelandic: Ætihvönn
Scientific: Angelica archangelica
Habitat: Fertile slopes in gorges, depressions, banks of springs and rivers, lake banks and islands.

Three species of angelica grow in Iceland and all of them are members of the carrot family (*Apiaceae*). The most common is the garden angelica and the other two are wild angelica (*Angelica sylvestris*) and Scots lovage (*Ligusticum scoticum*). Angelica is both good to eat and has medicinal properties, which is probably why its common and scientific names refer to angels. The angels are being shown gratitude for the use that angelica has provided people with. Another explanation for the angelic name is that in an old folk tale the archangel Gabriel appeared to a man during the Great Plague and saved him by showing him the angelica plant.

Angelica was widely used in Norway, where many settlers of Iceland came from. Angelica continued to be an important plant in Iceland after Settlement and is mentioned in Grágás, the earliest collection of laws in Iceland, which is testament to the plant's importance. Angelica is mentioned several times in the Icelandic Sagas, most notably in Fóstbræðra saga, where there is the famous episode when the sworn brothers Þorgeir and Þormóður went to collect angelica at Strandir in north-west Iceland. Þorgeir fell off the cliff Hornbjarg but managed to save himself by grabbing on to a stalk of angelica. The Icelandic name for angelica, *hvönn*, has given rise to numerous place names throughout Iceland, such as Hvanneyri, Hvannstóð, Hvannalindir, Hvanná, Hvannavallakvísl, Hvannavellir, Hvanndalabjarg, Hvanndalabyrða and Hvanndalir. There are also many place names associated with roots, rót in Icelandic, and it is likely that these refer to angelica roots which were the most commonly eaten roots in Iceland. These include Rótagil and Rótarfjallshnúkur which are both in Skaftafellssýslur in south-east Iceland.

Angelica was a great boon to people and all parts of the plant are edible and useable in some way or other. At the end of September people went out in the countryside to collect angelica roots and there are stories of people clashing with outlaws on these trips. A special digging tool, which was a metal spike with a wooden handle, was used. People also took along a special bag for the roots. The tool was used to loosen the earth around the root and then it was pulled up and the stalk was taken. The roots were stored separately in dry soil and buried deep enough to protect them from frost. They were eaten during the winter and dug up as needed. Roots were also buried underground in hay or kept in cold water if they only needed to be stored for a short time. The roots were used to distill a schnapps and the angelica imbued a strong and pleasant taste. To make angelica root schnapps you had to use two parts alcohol to one part angelica root. Adding half a teaspoon of angelica root schnapps to Icelandic herbal tea was considered healthy.

Angelica root was generally eaten raw with dried fish, butter or tallow or just on its own. The roots were sometimes chopped and boiled in skimmed milk, making a seasoned milk drink. In the Hornstrandir area in north-west Iceland the roots were put in sour whey and used in bread. Roots could also be treated in a mixture of salt and sugar and used in porridges.

The stalks had to be harvested in the early spring before they became wooden and they were eaten raw with fresh butter, put into soups and broths with angelica leaves and even rhubarb if available. The stalks were sometimes chopped and put into sour whey or eaten with skyr. Angelica stalks were laid in a sugar solution and eaten as a dessert, often with cream. Angelica leaves were used in soups and sauces for added taste and the leaves were also used in broths. Angelica seeds, dried and crushed, were sometimes used instead of a coffee substitute.

Angelica was believed to have a wide range of medicinal properties. It was thought to be able to cure upset stomachs, flatulence, intestinal parasites, side stitches, persistent coughs, chest pains, toothache and many other ailments. Angelica root was also used with other fragrant herbs to keep clothes fresh when they were stored in poor quality wooden chests. It was also thought that having angelica indoors could keep the smell of death at bay. The National Museum of Iceland has several flutes made from angelica stalks on display. A whole range of different tones could be produced by making the flutes in different lengths and thicknesses. Finally, children have used angelica stalks as toys since they are hollow and strong and can be turned into water pistols.

ICELAND MOSS

Icelandic: Fjallagrös
Scientific: Cetraria islandica
Habitat: Common in the highlands and lowlands.

Iceland moss, which despite its name is in fact a lichen, has been tremendously important to Icelanders through the ages. Without Iceland moss, life in Iceland would have been difficult in times of hardship as moss provides carbohydrates, minerals and has anti-bacterial properties. In Norway lichen was mainly used in times of adversity and as fodder for pigs. The Norwegians were able to grow cereals and therefore were not reliant on the carbohydrates obtained from lichen. The climate made it difficult to grow cereal in Iceland and therefore Icelanders had to use lichen as a source of carbohydrates. The Icelanders did not immediately realize the importance of lichen and no laws were made concerning lichen until the Law of Iceland was introduced in 1281, shortly after Iceland came under Norwegian sovereignty.

Trips into the mountains to collect lichen had an air of great adventure about them and there are numerous folk tales of encounters with outlaws and the hidden people on such expeditions. Trips to collect lichen were also opportunities for romance, as labourers from different farms met and spent many nights on the mountain under the magical midnight sun of the Icelandic summer. It was considered a great honour when young people were finally allowed to go on their first trip to gather lichen.

Trips to gather lichen were undertaken in the early summer, before the haymaking season, around mid to late June. At this time of year the nights were bright and it was easy to gather lichen through the night. People went into the mountains in groups of 10-20, one or more from each farm. The farm workers took with them horses, tents and other necessities and were away from home for a week or two. It was thought safest to be in big groups as they often crossed paths with outlaws, thieves and vagrants. Damp conditions were best for gathering lichen, preferably when it was raining, but in dry spells they gathered at night. The lichen could be seen more easily in wet conditions when it rose clear above the low vegetation. If dry, the lichen contracts into the moss which sticks to it when the lichen is pulled from the ground, It is also rougher to touch and more fragile and can irritate the hands of people gathering the lichen.

The lichen was first dried and cleaned, which was a task for children and old people. The lichen was laid out in trays and cleaned. Lichen had a wide range of uses. It was commonly used to make bread after being chopped with a herb knife or torn apart by hand after boiling water was poured on to the lichen. When making bread, the lichen was boiled and kneaded into rye dough with sour whey or a dollop of sourdough and the bread was then boiled for a long time. Lichen flat bread and lichen boiled bread were well known but lichen rye bread was easily the most common variety.

Lichen broths were generally made of water and flour was added if available. If barley was added, it needed to simmer for longer. Sometimes rye flour was added. This broth was eaten throughout Iceland, with skyr and often with steamed milk. Many foreign visitors to Iceland were given lichen broth on their travels and described it in their travel journals.

> *"For the foreigner, lichen broth is not only the healthiest dish but is also the tastiest of all Icelandic foods,"* it says in a travel journal from the early 19th century.   Henderson, 1957(1818):72

To make lichen milk, the lichen was sugared and boiled in milk and this was considered a great delicacy. Sometimes it was served as a soup. Another common food was curdled lichen and this was considered good eating, but jellied lichen, which was just water boiled with lichen until it congealed, was only eaten in times of need. Lichen was believed to extend the storage life of food and blood sausage, bread and rye bread could all be stored longer with lichen. Lichen was thought to give a bread a softer texture and make it taste better. At Bjarneyjar in western Iceland during the infamously cold winter of 1918-1919 when temperatures dropped to -30°C, the barrels containing the cured foods froze solid and all the blood puddings were ruined, except those made with lichen.

The medicinal properties of lichen are incontrovertible. Lichen was widely used in lichen tea, especially to alleviate stomach aches or chest pains. Lichen tea was also used as a refreshment and many other plants could be added to enhance the flavour, e.g. wild thyme, yarrow, mountain avens and alpine lady's mantle.

Lichen has long been used as a dye. It gives a yellowish colour and a red colour if the wool is soaked in cow urine and changed every other day. It

was called Icelandic cardinal red. A piece of yarn was placed into the lichen solution and was left there for an hour and then put into urine. Every day the yarn was exposed to the air and then dunked into a new batch of urine. This was done until the yarn had turned red. This "cow-urine red" was not considered to be beautiful, it soon became discoloured and had an unpleasant smell.

Outlaws and hidden people often crossed paths with people out gathering lichen in the mountains. Here is a folk tale about people gather lichen from Skörð in northern Iceland:

At Skörð, an area of the mountains between Skagafjörður and Húnavatnssýsla, there is a farm called Selhólar. Close to the farm is a pond called Djúpatjörn, or Deep Pond. The pond is full of trout, both large and small, but whenever nets are placed in the pond, they are always found the next morning scrunched up or torn to shreds on the edge of the pond. People have tried to lay nets many times but the outcome is always the same.

> *"Once upon a time there was a group of people out collecting lichen and they camped next to the pond. One morning a girl left her tent at sunrise. She saw five boats on the pond, with two men in each except for the largest boat which had three. They were pulling up the nets and hauling in a large catch. She knew they were the hidden people and watched them for a long time. But when she glanced away, she never laid eyes on them again."*

> Jón Árnason, 1961a, Volume 1, p. 40

Krækiber

BERRIES

Iceland is home to several species of berries which were used by people in the past. These are crowberry (*Empetrum nigrum*), bog bilberry (*Vaccinium uliginosum*), common bilberry (*Vaccinium myrtillus*), stone bramble (*Rubus saxatilis*) and wild strawberry (*Fragaria vesca*). Berrypicking was usually left to children and the elderly. Crowberries and bilberries were the most important berries for households as Grágás, the first collection of Icelandic laws, contained laws on picking berries.

> *"A person may collect berries and dulse on another person's land, but if he takes them without permission, he will receive a penalty of three marks."*

The later Law of Iceland, Jónsbók, said

> *"A man may not pick berries without permission on another man's land and take them home. If he does so, he must pay twice the amount and also for lichen if he collects it."*

CROWBERRY

Icelandic: Krækilyng
Scientific: Empetrum nigrum
Habitat: Wide variety of habitats: heathland, gravel hills, expanses of moss,
lava fields and even bogs. Very common.

Crowberries were picked during the summer and eaten fresh or stored for the winter in skyr. The berries were thought to taste better in skyr and stayed fresh longer. Eating too many crowberries could lead to headaches and chest pains. The berries were also soaked in water and the berry juice seeped into the water, and this was considered to be a refreshing drink on its own or mixed with sour whey. Berry juice, both fresh and curdled in winter, was also a delicacy. The berries were put in a muslin cloth and squeezed and the juice was used in soups or broths and stored in bottles.

The Icelandic annals say that Bishop Páll of Skálholt made wine from crowberries in 1203. This was presumably owing to a shortage of sacramental wine. The Bishop of Trondheim asked the Pope to allow people to make sacramental bread from something other than wheat and to use ale instead of wine at holy communion but the Pope rejected this plea and the art of making crowberry wine was then lost.

Crowberries have been used for medicinal purposes and they contain both tannins and vitamins. Berry juice cures sores and bleeding in the digestive system. The juice can also be used to regulate bowel movements in children. Crowberries are nutritious in moderate quantities but over-indulgence can lead to constipation and a lack of appetite. Recent studies have shown that crowberries are an excellent source of anti-oxidants.

The same juice used for soups and broths was also used to dye wool and it produced an attractive purple colour, which was not very durable, however. A yellow dye produced by the plant was longer lasting. The shrubs used to be used for lighting fires, especially by the seashore. Crowberry shrubs were also used as padding in houses and bedding although it was not considered suited to this, and for decorating Christmas trees. Christmas trees were homemade, painted and then decorated with sprigs of plants such as juniper, crowberry or bearberry. Crowberry shrubs were believed to be able to keep away fleas and lice and were placed in beds and other bedding. The older Icelandic name, "louse heather" may be a reference to this belief, but the small leaves were also thought to resemble lice. There was an old folk belief that said a bumper crop of berries heralded a harsh winter.

Bog Bilberry

BOG BILBERRY & COMMON BILBERRY

Icelandic: Bláberjalyng
Scientific: Vaccinium uliginosum
Habitat: Heathland, depressions and slopes, sometimes on hummocks in bogs. Common.

Icelandic: Aðalbláberjalyng
Scientific: Vaccinium myrtillus
Habitat: Depressions in slopes, heathland and woodland, mainly in snow rich regions. Common
in locations where snow cover is guaranteed throughout winter. In less snowy districts the Bilberry
is not found in the lowlands, but usually in snowbeds higher up on the mountain slopes.

It is not always clear whether historical sources are referring to the bog bilberry or the common bilberry when talking about gathering berries in general and the two species will be discussed together.

Bog bilberry juice was often poured on to skyr. Ebenezer Henderson, a Scottish traveller who visited Iceland at the beginning of the 19th century described Icelandic cuisine at the time as follows:

> *"The everyday diet of Icelanders is terribly monotonous. For break-*
> *fast they eat skyr, which is made from curdled milk, similar to our*
> *Scottish curds, with the exception that it has a sour taste. With the*
> *skyr they eat great quantities of milk or cream and sometimes*
> *they give it a peculiar flavour by squeezing juice from bilberries or*
> *juniper berries on to it."*

> *Henderson, 1957(1818):67*

People ate bilberries fresh, on their own or with skyr or cream and they were not stored for the winter as crowberries were. Bilberries were considered to be more of a delicacy than crowberries and were served as a treat for guests with sugar and cream. Bilberries were also mixed with whipped cream and if chocolate was then added, it was a truly delicious delicacy. Juice was also made from bilberries and used in tasty soups and broths.

In Iceland people made a juice which was left to simmer until all the water evaporated. The residue was then used like cream of tartar in cooking. Bilberry leaves were used in tea. Bilberry jam is a more recent product. Bog bilberry was used for dyeing with other substances and the blue colour was reasonably durable. Common bilberry produced a blue that was not quite as stable and a yellow colour could be obtained from the leaves of bog bilberry. Bog bilberry leaves contain acids which make them suitable for using as a dye.

Common Bilberry

STONE BRAMBLE

Icelandic: Hrútaber
Scientific: Rubus saxatilis
Grassy slopes and woodland. Rather common.

Although stone bramble is common, it is never numerous in any one place. The berries contain large pips which are unpleasant to bite into and this may have restricted their use as a food. The berries are also rather sour and are never as numerous as crowberries which means they were not as popular for eating. They were probably used due to their beautiful colour. Stone bramble was possibly little used in Iceland but there are examples of the berries having been used in soups. In a set of memoirs written in Dalasýsla in western Iceland in 1880 it was reported that berries were heated, put into a cloth and pressed and the juice used in a jelly. This jelly was then used as a topping on small puff pastry cakes. In recent years people have made a bramble jelly out of it. The plant has been used for healing purposes and folk remedies include wrapping runners from the plant around affected areas to cure rheumatism. In Icelandic the runners of the stone bramble are known as *tröllareipi*, or troll ropes, due to the folk belief that they could be used to tie down evil spirits.

COMMON JUNIPER

Icelandic: Einir
Scientific: Juniperus communis
Habitat: Heathland, lava fields, brushwood and hill edges. Common.

Common juniper is Iceland's only native conifer. It has small berries which are formed by leaves at the end of the branch fusing around the inflorescence. The flowers become mature in their first autumn but do not bloom until the spring. In the first year the berries are green but by the second year they have turned blue-blaack and have ripened. The same female shrub can have flowers, green berries and ripe berries.

The juniper has always been considered a mysterious plant as there are myriad folk beliefs attached to juniper bushes and the use of juniper berries. It was said that you could use a juniper bush to find thieves and that the juniper and the mountain ash were deadly enemies or complete opposites. If a ship was constructed out of mountain ash, juniper had to be used too, because mountain ash would drag the ship to the bottom while the juniper would pull it to the surface. It was also though that if a house was built using juniper and mountain ash it would burn down.

Juniper was much used in the past, both its berries and branches. The berries were sold by weight and one could quickly load a horse with juniper berries in places such as Þórsmörk. When the birch woodlands became depleted, people began gather juniper bushes and this reduced its distribution. In Borgarfjörður in western Iceland people celebrated Juniper Sunday at the end of May when everyone went out to pick juniper berries. The berries were not sold in Borgarfjörður but were given as presents to people who didn't have access to such rich berry country as Borgarfjörður. Juniper was also pulled up by the roots for other purposes and this led to the eradication of the plant in some areas. Juniper berries were used as food and drink. They were eaten with butter instead of fish and the juice was mixed with skyr. Juniper berries were used to add flavour to gin, schnapps, beer and the Dutch liquor Jenever. Indeed, in those days Icelandic schnapps flavoured with juniper was a kind of Icelandic Jenever. Farmers let the berries soak in schnapps and then ate them in the mornings before breakfast. There are many tales of soaking herbs in schnapps and people having a tipple for the good of their health. Juniper schnapps was supposed to be drunk in the mornings as a remedy for chest pains, and smoke from juniper incense was supposed to be healthy.

Priests in Barðastrandarsýsla in north-west Iceland burned juniper and brewed a drink similar to coffee, which was supposed to be an effective remedy for thick blood and chest pains. Other people boiled the berries and made a drink which was good against tuberculosis and chest pains. A poultice made from juniper berries was an effective treatment for burns. Pregnant women were not allowed to consume juniper berries, and abroad there are various folk beliefs linking juniper to fertility and miscarriage. In the 18th century a movement emerged whose aim was to persuade Icelanders to give up drinking coffee in favour of a juniper drink.

Juniper does not appear to have been an important source of dye in Iceland but it could be used to produce a yellow-brown colour mixed with other materials.

Juniper was also used as incense to eliminate unpleasant smells indoors, and it was thought that infectious diseases could be kept at bay with juniper smoke. Smoke from juniper berries was wafted over pregnant women to keep the devil at a safe distance. There were few places in Borgarfjörður where juniper was as common as at Geitland, and people from all over the district gathered juniper and used it as incense to freshen up crowded living rooms. Juniper was also used in the past as a cane to beat disobedient children and they might be threatened with a thrashing with a urine-soaked juniper branch. This was also considered a remedy for excessive itching. At the Althing, the Icelandic parliament, juniper branches were used to whip criminals.

Juniper and other evergreens were also used to decorate homemade Christmas trees and the juniper is the subject of the popular Christmas song *"Göngum við í kringum einiberjarunn, einiberjarunn, einiberjarunn"*, similar in meaning to the English nursery rhyme *"Here We Go Round the Mulberry Bush"* albeit sung to a different tune. The tradition of Christmas trees was brought over from Denmark in the late 19th century, where juniper was a traditional decoration, and this custom undoubtedly came to Iceland with the Christmas tree.

BEARBERRY

Icelandic: Sortulyng
Scientific: Arctostaphylos uva-ursi
Habitat: Dwarf-shrub heaths and woodland. Common.

The Icelandic name for bearberry, *sortulyng,* or black heather, is undoubtedly an old name and is linked to the fact that black or a dark-coloured dye could be obtained from the berries. Other Icelandic folk names include *músaberjalyng* and *músaber* or mouse berry as it was believed that mice were fond of the berries. Another traditional Icelandic name associates the plant with lice. In the old days lice were a widespread problem and it was thought that if people ate bearberries they would immediately become infested with lice. To ward off lice people put lice heather, a folk name for crowberry, in their bedding.

There is little evidence of bearberries being used for medicinal purposes in Iceland, although people did chew the leaves to treat various mouth ailments and sores as doing so increased saliva production and this was supposed to heal sores. Bearberry leaves were also added to tobacco to make it go further in times of hardship.

However, bearberry was widely used as a dye in the past. Travellers in the 18th century described in their journals that the populace always appeared to be in mourning. This was on account of the bearberry dye which produced black, grey-green, grey-yellow and blue-grey colours. Perhaps people were in mourning, or at least in low spirits, as the period from the Middle Ages to the 19th century was a time of adversity in Iceland and black was therefore an appropriate colour. During this period people generally stopped travelling to Norway to buy colourful garments and just wore black. The Middle Ages have been called "*the era of no colour*" owing to the fact that black was the dominant colour for clothes in Iceland, indeed not just in the Middle Ages but up until far more recently.

Bearberry could also be used to produce a red colour but this required the use of cow urine. Bearberry also contains tannin which makes it a good dye and also for tanning leather. Young girls used bearberries to colour calf leather for their best shoes.

People used bearberries mixed with willow (*Salix sp.*) and mud to make ink. The residue from the bearberry dye could be used as ink if mixed with iron or mud. The willow made the ink more shiny and durable. Some people also made ink from soot by dissolving the soot in water and mixing it with calf's blood. This ink was not very durable. There are numerous folk beliefs associated with bearberries and it was believed to protect people from ghosts.

HEATHER

Icelandic: Beitilyng
Scientific: Calluna vulgaris
Habitat: Heathland and slopes. Common.

The most common use for heather in Iceland was as a dye. A range of shades of yellows and greens can be obtained from heather through various techniques and using substances to mix it with. The best method was to collect heather in the summer and use it when it was fresh as the colours obtained from dry heather were browner. The heather has to be boiled to obtain the dye. Other uses included chopping the heather and using it as fodder for cows. In some areas it was chopped for firewood where other sources of wood were scarce. It later years people began decorating Christmas trees with heather and other evergreens but this did not become commonplace until the beginning of the 20th century. People also drank water infused with heather and heather tea. One folk belief was that heather could foretell the winter weather. A shoot sometimes sprouts out of the cluster of flowers and it therefore appears that heather does not flower at the top of the plant. If the heather flowers all the way to the top, it heralded a harsh winter, but if the ends of the shoots have no flowers the winter is nothing to fear.

LICHEN

Icelandic: Litunarskófir
Scientific: Parmelia sp.
Habitat: Common all over Iceland on rocks.

Iceland is home to three species of lichen of the genus *Parmelia*: salted shield lichen or crottal (*P. saxatilis*), purple rock lichen (*P. omphalodes*) and netted shield lichen (*P. sulcata*). All three species were used for dyeing and they were used equally, depending on what was locally available. It is unlikely that people distinguished between the different types of lichen and instead referred to them all by the vernacular name litunarmosi or "dyeing moss." They all contain lichen acids which make them suitable for dyeing. Purple rock lichen was possibly the species that was most commonly used as it is generally more common and that is why it is called litunarskóf or "dyeing lichen" in Icelandic.

As the Icelandic name suggests, lichen was chiefly used in Iceland, and indeed elsewhere, for dyeing. Light and dark browns as well as red-browns could be obtained from lichen.

The Saga of Finnbogi the Strong mentions moss:

> "It is said that on the same day Þorgerður gave birth, Syrpa sent her husband to look for moss because she made many things she needed for her foster-daughter."
>
> Finnboga saga ramma, 1985:626

It is likely that moss actually refers to lichen.

Books from the 17th century mention that various kinds of moss were used to dye clothes and this might in fact be referring to lichen. According to folklore you couldn't bring lichen close to the meadow as it would kill cow on the farm.

Various methods were used to dye clothes with lichen. The traditional Icelandic method was to put lichen and wool into a pot together, pour in cold water, leave it for a while and then boil it for several hours. Other people put lichen in a muslin gauze to obtain a more even colour One source states that in Iceland people knew how to procure a light purple colour by soaking the lichen in rank urine with salt and then rolling the lichen into small balls with lemon juice.

There is little evidence that lichens were used for medicinal purposes in the past. There was a midwife known as Grasa-Þórunn in the mid-19th century. She may have been talking about lichen when she described visiting a graveyard where a body was being dug up and she saw that the corpse was wearing stockings. The corpse was badly decomposed except for the legs. The stocking were coloured with something she called steinurt or stone plant, and following this discovery she used this plant extensively to heal wounds and for its preservative qualities. In more recent times lichen has been used in a herbal remedy made from lupins invented by Ævar Jóhannesson as a treatment for cancer.

When settlers arrived in Iceland in 9th century they would have been familiar with lichens and could continue the tradition of using it as a dye as they did in Norway.

WOOD CRANESBILL

Icelandic: Blágresi
Scientific: Geranium sylvaticum
Habitat: Grassy slopes, sheltered locations, ravines, birch copses,
snowbeds in the lower mountains.

Wood cranesbill was almost certainly more common in the past when woodland was more widespread in Iceland. Blue is the colour of royalty and the rich and it is therefore a difficult colour to obtain naturally. As far as is known there are no species of plant in Iceland which produce a blue dye. In the old days it was thought possible to be able to get blue from wood cranesbill. There is a story about an old woman from Skagaströnd in northern Iceland who knew how to get a blue dye but she refused to reveal the secret and took it with her to the grave. Some people attribute the knowledge of obtaining blue dye from wood cranesbill entirely to the people of the West Fjords, but this knowledge has been lost today. Dark colours could also be obtained, as indicated by the plant's alternative Icelandic name, sortugras, or black grass. In eastern Iceland wood cranesbill was used as a black dye instead of bearberry. The blue colour mentioned in the Icelandic sagas is from woad (*Isatis tinctorum*) and by the 18th century indigo (*Indigfera tinctorum*) was being imported as a dye. The blue colour from wood cranesbill was in reality probably grey, as grey can sometimes appear blue among other colours. Furthermore, what people in the past considered to be blue is probably not the same as today.

Lady's Bedstraw

Northern Bedstraw

MADDER

Icelandic: Gulmaðra
Scientific: Galium verum
Habitat: Dry, grassy plains, heaths and woodland. Common.

Icelandic: Krossmaðra
Scientific: Galium borale
Habitat: Grassy heaths and slopes. Common in the south and west, rare elsewhere.

Iceland is home to several species of madder. This book will focus on lady's bedstraw and northern bedstraw as other species of madder have not been used by people in Iceland. The Icelandic name maðra, clearly related to the English madder, is likely the source of places names such as Möðruvellir and Möðrufell in Eyjafjörður in northern Iceland, where lady's bedstraw is abundant. There are various folk beliefs associated with lady's bedstraw in Iceland. A problem faced by housewives in Eyjafjörður was that milk tended to curdle if lady's bedstraw grew in the meadows.

This was often blamed on witchcraft practiced by the neighbours or given another supernatural explanation. However lady's bedstraw, like common butterwort, does curdle milk. Madder probably occurred in Iceland at the time of Settlement but pollen counts have shown that lady's bedstraw increased dramatically after Settlement.

Leaves of lady's bedstraw were believed to help induce sweating and in the 19th century it was considered to be a good way of warding off scurvy.

All madder roots contain the red pigments *alezarin* and *purpurin* and this makes them good sources of red dye. The roots of Icelandic madder are small and an enormous quantity was needed to make the dye. In the last few centuries Icelanders imported common madder (*Rubia tinctorum*) root from abroad which has larger roots. A travel journal from the 18th century mentioned that the roots of lady's bedstraw and northern bedstraw were used as a red dye and other parts of the lady's bedstraw were used as a yellow dye. The author of the journal said that many people he had spoken to had studied the uses of madder, which indicates that it was a well-known medicinal plant.

Lady's Bedstraw

BOGBEAN

Icelandic: Horblaðka
Scientific: Menyanthes trifoliata
Habitat: Bogs, ditches and pond margins. Rather common.

Bogbean was probably never used for human consumption but it was used for medicinal purposes. It was said that it had divine power and that it could cure hepatitis and stomach ailments and was also a tonic for body and mind.

Bogbean was used to flavour beer and the root was smoked instead of tobacco in Rangárvallasýsla in southern Iceland. Other Icelandic names associate the plant with packhorses because areas where bogbean grew were suitable for cutting turf to place under packs saddles. It was also thought safe to cross marshes where bogbean abounded as the root system was so dense that it prevented the horses from sinking into the mire and formed a floating expanse of grass. Marshes were a great obstacle to travel in the old days and people used vegetation as a guide to where the safest route lay.

NORTHERN DOCK

Icelandic: Njóli
Scientific: Rumex longifolius
Habitat: Introduced, stabilized alien in populated areas, waste grounds, dumps, road-
sides, sometimes forming continuous cover in abandoned home fields. Common.

Analyses of pollen in soil before and after Settlement show that Northern Dock is one of the plants that was brought to Iceland by early settlers and today it has a close association with human habitation.

The tradition of eating northern dock in Iceland does not date back very far. People started eating it in the 18th century but it was not widespread. People ate it instead of cabbage and added it to tasty and healthy soups and broths. Northern dock does not appear to have been commonly known as an edible plant in the 20th century. Mashed dock and white sauce made from dock became known in the last century and were probably Danish traditions introduced by merchants or Icelanders educated in Copenhagen.

Northern dock is a member of the knotweed family which all contain oxalic acid which makes them good for making dye. It produces a yellow and yellow-green colour if the leaves are fresh, chopped into small pieces and mixed with the flower of the meadow buttercup. The mixture is then placed between fabrics in a dyeing pot, alum is added and the contents are boiled for a good while. Human urine is then added to make the colours more distinct and this colour was often used in children's sweaters.

Northern dock could also be used to produce green colours with the help of copper. Copper was commonly used as a dye but before it became available in powered form, copper or iron pots were used. In Eyjafjörður, the hardened stalks of dock were used in the autumn as reels in a loom.

Dock root could be used a laxative and was known as a medicinal plant in the 17th century and was used to treat hepatitis. Various folk beliefs are associated with dock. For example, it was thought safe to start hay-making once the stalk had become wooden. Dock could also indicate whether a girl was a virgin or not but how this was done is not quite clear.

COMMON SORREL

Icelandic: Túnsúra
Scientific: Rumex acetosa
Habitat: Grassy plains, fertilized home fields, heathland and fertile slopes.
Very common.

Common sorrel is believed to have been in Iceland before Settlement and pollen counts indicate that it increased and spread when humans arrived here.

Common sorrel was eaten in the past, although local knowledge varied from place to place. It was used in soups made from succulent herbs, in salads and also mashed, as was common in Denmark.

A foreign traveller to Iceland got to taste sorrel on his journeys here in the early 19th century. At an extravagant daytime banquet at Viðey, the guests were served half a calf with meats soured with boiled sorrel and sugar. In Borgarfjörður a traveller was served sorrel sauce with his roast.

Sorrel was also used as a drink. The leaves were soaked in water and the juice seeped into the water. This drink was used instead of sour whey but it had a short shelf-life and soon went off and became mouldy, especially if the weather was warm. As a medicine sorrel was used to stimulate appetite and to treat ergot poisoning.

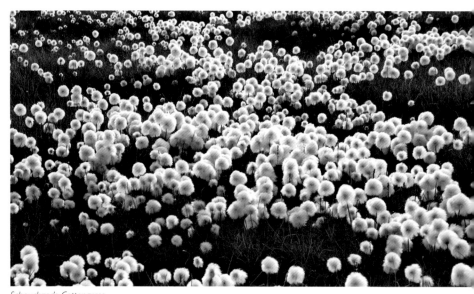

Scheuchzer's Cottongrass

COMMON COTTONGRASS & SCHEUCHZER'S COTTONGRASS

Common Cottongrass | Icelandic: Klófífa
Scientific: Eriophorum angustifolium
Habitat: Bogs, mires and moist lake banks. | Very common.

Scheuchzer's Cottongrass | Icelandic: Hrafnafífa
Scientific: Eriophorum scheuchzeri
Habitat: Roadside, ditches, open peat soil, sandy riversides, springs and bogs. | Common.

Cottongrass was used to make wicks for fish oil lamps. It was gathered in the summer by the children. The wicks were fashioned from cottongrass and had to last the entire winter. Linen rags could not be used as wicks as they produced an unpleasant smell. The wick was coiled in the upper chamber of the lamp and the other end emerged at the opening where it was lit. The species of cotton grass used depended on which was more readily available although common cottongrass was considered easier to manipulate into wicks than Scheuzer's cottongrass. This kind of wick was used until cotton twine began to be imported and replaced cottongrass. The wicks were twisted with the fingers and bound. Cottongrass seeds got in the way when it was spun, but an old trick practised in Skagafjörður in northern Iceland was to leave the cottongrass on the floor of the barn overnight. The mice would eat the seeds and leave the cottongrass behind. This technique was also known in southern Iceland.

Cottongrass was also used as a stuffing. It was comfortable but not very durable and was therefore called poor man's pillow. In a travel journal from the 18th century it was advised against riding through marshes where cottongrass predominated as the plant had a poor root system and the marsh was therefore soft underfoot.

Common Cottongrass

DOWNY BIRCH

Icelandic: Birki
Scientific: Betula pubescens
Habitat: Forms scrub or woods in moderately dry soil from the lowlands up to 400-450 m. Growth form varies with local climate: dense and low scrub prevails along coast and in stormy and oceanic climate, taller brushwood and trees further inland, especially in more continental areas. Common.

Downy Birch is widespread in Iceland as a bush or a tree which can reach up to 12 metres in height. The bark is red-brown and flakes off. Birch was heavily used after Settlement and pollen counts show that birch pollen decreased dramatically after Iceland was settled. Birch was used to construct houses, as fuel and as charcoal, and the decrease in pollen is undoubtedly linked to these factors as well as winter grazing.

Birch bark was widely used for tanning as it contains high quantities of tannic acid. The bark also gave the leather a reddish-brown tone and it made it denser. Birch was used as a dye and different methods could be used to obtain yellow-green, grey-green, green and yellow from the leaves, while the bark could produce pink-brown, grey and coffee-brown hues. Bark dyeing required large quantities of urine and the leaves had to be boiled for a long time.

Birch leaves in tea were thought to be good remedies against jaundice and scurvy.

Knots in the trunk were fashioned into tobacco boxes and other small knick-knacks. Later, from the middle of the 20th century, people began to use birch trees as Christmas tree and branches were added and furnished with Christmas decorations. Using the outer bark of birch never seems to have been common, although it is mentioned in agricultural laws from the 15th century, which indicates that people used bark in the early days of Settlement before the forests became depleted or bark was imported.

WHITE CLOVER

Icelandic: Hvítsmári
Scientific: Trifolium repens
Habitat: Grass plains, slopes, hillsides and cultivated home fields. Common.
Native with wide distribution in the north, naturalized alien in some other regions.

White clover is a widespread flower in Iceland and had many uses in the old days. It was gathered in the spring before the leaves had sprouted, because once it was summer the flower was bitter-tasting and became inedible. Clover was dug up using small wooden or metal hooks called a clover hook. After the roots were dug up, they were left for a day before being put in a barrel or other wooden container. The runners or stolons from the clover had many different uses and were eaten with dried fish, dulse, milk or butter. Stolons were also delicious with whipped milk. In the Mývatn district in north-east Iceland the roots were eaten in years of hardship and the stolons were eaten with butter. Clover was also boiled in milk and drunk in the evenings to help people sleep, but clover was also looked upon as food for poor people.

White clover flowers were used as a dye. They were gathered when the flower was in bloom and then dried. The flowers produced a pale yellow colour if alum was added to the solution. Adding urine produced a dark tone. In order to get a greener colour, non-native plants needed to be added.

White clover leaves have three leaflets but four-leaf clovers do occur and finding one is said to bring great luck to the finder. Four-leaf clovers were kept in sacred books to enhance their power and some people believed they could be used to grant wishes.

> *"A clover with more than three leaves probably does not exist, that is why its Latin name is trifolium. But if one does find a four-leaf clover, it can open any lock by holding it to the keyhole or inserting it and blowing into it. This will open any lock."*
>
> Jón Árnason, 1956, Volume 4, p. 23

DANDELION

Icelandic: Túnfífll
Scientific: Taraxacum spp.
Habitat: Cultivated home fields and grassland, at the base of house walls,
hollows in heathland, and snowbeds in mountains. Very common.

Dandelions take their English name from the French *dent-de-lion* or lion's tooth. Pollen counts have shown that dandelions spread after Settlement and it may have been here already or have been brought here by the first settlers. In the 18th century scholar Björn Halldórsson recommended that people sowed dandelions next to the farmhouse, an idea which would hardly have occurred to anyone, since dandelions were generally looked on as weeds rather than decorative flowers.

Eating dandelion roots was well known in past and was mentioned in written sources from the 17th century. The roots were cooked over embers or eaten raw. Dandelion leaves were also commonly used in salads in early spring. Leaves were used in broths to help stomach ailments. The leaves had to be chopped finely and boiled in whey or water mixed with milk. People were advised to eat dandelion broth in the aftermath of the great volcanic eruptions of 1783 and it was said to have cured most ailments within a few days. This tradition was kept alive and dandelion leaves have been used in salads ever since. Dandelion is used as a remedy for breathing difficulties and heart complaints. The milky sap from the stalks was said to be able to remove warts.

After flowering the flower closes while the seeds are developing and then opens to reveal the downy seed head. These dandelion clocks have been the playthings of children for centuries and the stalks have also been used to make play necklaces and decorations.

HERB-PARIS

Icelandic: Ferlaufungur
Scientific: Paris quadrifolia
Habitat: Brushwood and lava fissures. Rare. Protected by law.

Herb-paris is protected in Iceland. Numerous folk beliefs are associated with herb-paris and it was considered sacred. The berries are poisonous and were known in Icelandic as *úlfsber*, or wolfberries, as in Scandinavia poisonous berries were associated with wolves. Herb-paris has several traditional names in Icelandic connected to the belief that it could open locked doors, e.g *lásagras* (lock grass), *þjófagras* (thief grass) and *þjófarót* (thief root). The plant was also believed to have the power to help women during difficult childbirth.

WILD THYME

Icelandic: Blóðberg
Scientific: Thymus praecox subsp. arcticus
Habitat: Gravel hills, dry heathland and slopes, cliffsides and rock ledges.

Sour whey mixed with water was a common drink in Iceland. It was flavoured with a range of different plants, including wild thyme which made the drink refreshing and delicious. A broth made from a range of herbs was known as *heimate* or "home-made tea", and thyme was a common ingredient in this drink. In the 19th century people used to dry various plants, including thyme, in the autumn and store them in muslin bags over the winter and use them to make hot drinks.

Wild thyme was well known as a medicine and as a refreshment. In the 18th century wild thyme was considered one of the best medicinal herbs from which to make a remedy for various complaints. It was believed to fortify the stomach and head, open up the lungs, cure liver ailments and a weak spleen and could cure dizziness. Thyme tea also appears to have been an effective antidote to hangovers as in a travel journal from the 18th century it says:

> *"Many people mix it with other herbs in tea and it is good for headaches brought on by intoxication the day before."*
>
> Mohr, 1786:196

A potion made of wild thyme and madder was used to cure milk fever in cows. New studies on thyme have indicated that it contains active essential oils, tannic acids, and various chemicals which are anti-bacterial, works as an expectorant, soothes cramping and reduces flatulence. More recently wild thyme tea has been used as a remedy for colds and flu.

Wild thyme was used to drive fleas out of houses by boiling it and dispersing it over the floor or by burning it to give off a pleasant aroma. This undoubtedly improved the smell indoors at the same time. Thyme does not appear to have been used as a seasoning until more recently, and it is possible that thyme imported from overseas was used in Icelandic kitchens before Icelandic thyme. In some places thyme or a broth made from it was used with sour whey in the autumn. Thyme was also used to produce a yellow dye.

YARROW

Icelandic: Vallhumall
Scientific: Achillea millefolium
Habitat: Dry slopes and flats, often in sandy soil. Common.

Pollen counts show that yarrow first arrived in Iceland at the time of Settlement. It may have been cultivated here and used instead of hops when brewing beer. It could have been grown in the garden at the bishop's residence at Skálholt or been brought there by accident among goods shipped from abroad.

Yarrow was often used in "home-made tea" with wild thyme. It was hung to dry on a thread and then boiled in water when required. Wild thyme and mountain avens leaves were added to the mix and could be a stored for a long time without losing their potency.

Yarrow is known as medicinal plant in Iceland. The flowers were dried in flour and the powder was sprinkled into open wounds to help them heal better. The entire plant, or just the flower, was placed in a pot and boiled with butter and used as an ointment. In Skaftafellssýslur in south-east Iceland, yarrow is considered to be one of the most effective local medicines. Medical advice was often influenced by folk belief and superstition. An old recipe for a medicine made from yarrow was as follows:

> *"Take a burnt mouse skin, chopped yarrow, crushed pepper and soil from a graveyard; shake these together in a box, clean the wound thoroughly with puppy urine and sprinkle the powder over the wound."*
>
> Jónas Jónasson, 1945:328

Yet the healing effect of yarrow is not mere invention, since studies of its effectiveness have indicated that it contains numerous active ingredients which have an effect on swelling, are anti-bacterial and beneficial to the stomach.

According to folklore, if yarrow was taken on a sea voyage it would prevent the ship from being sunk by whales.

SEA THRIFT

Icelandic: Geldingahnappur
Scientific: Armeria maritima
Habitat: Sand, gravel and eroded land, sometimes in dry grassland or heaths.
Very common, not least in the barren interior.

Sea thrift is a common flower in sandy and gravely areas of Iceland. In eastern Iceland the poor used flower buds as filling in cushions when they had nothing else to use. The cushions were comfortable for a while but were not very durable. Although scarcely considered to be edible, the roots were nevertheless nutritious if boiled long enough to soften them, sometimes in milk. The root of thrift seems to have only been eaten in times of hardship, as was the case with the root of moss campion as they are often mentioned together.

> *"All that ends up in the belly is food, besides the roots of moss campion and sea thrift."*
>
> Guðmundur Jónsson, 1930:32

This old saying indicates that eating these roots was considered the last resort.

MOSS CAMPION

Icelandic: Lambagras
Scientific: Silene acaulis
Habitat: Sandy or gravelly, usually in dry soil in exposed locations
on hills and rock ledges, poor pastures. Very common.

The roots of the moss campion had similar uses to those of sea thrift. The roots were eaten during famines and were dug up in the spring, boiled in water and eaten with butter. In Kjósarsýsla in south-west Iceland, moss campion roots were used instead of flour in times of hardship. Moss campion flowers first on the side facing the sun. When in full bloom it gives off a pleasant fragrance.

There was an old saying:

> *"All that ends up in the belly is food, besides scaly pike skin and raw moss campion roots."*
>
> Jón Árnason, 1961b, Volume 2, p. 532

ROSEROOT

Icelandic: Burnirót
Scientific: Rhodiola rosea
Habitat: Since the Roseroot cannot survive continuous grazing it is usually found in steep cliffs, gorges or lake islands not accessible to sheep. Widespread.

Sheep are particularly fond of roseroot and it is therefore mainly found on cliffs, ravines and islands which are out of the reach of livestock. Roseroot is an effective medicinal plant and an ointment made from roseroot and butter was good for relieving pain and could cure old wounds. It was said to cure headaches by just washing the head with an infusion made of roseroot. Roseroot was used to treat milk fever in cattle after calving. The plant was chopped into milk and given to the cows to drink.

Roseroot has also been used to dye wool green by boiling it in small pieces with the wool and alum. If it is used like bark when treating animal hides, it gives the leather an attractive yellow tone. There are many folk beliefs associated with roseroot. It was supposed to be placed in the bed of a women giving birth and touching the root would ensure a trouble-free birth.

> "Roseroot has many beneficial uses. It must be held with a clean cloth when digging it up and the grass must be cut away because it has an evil nature. Roseroot may not be exposed outdoors; it should be stored in hallowed ground. One should wear it during the day but keep it at the foot of the bed at night, and then one will experience no troubles."

> Jónas Jónasson, 1945:409

MARSH-MARIGOLD

Icelandic: Hófsóley
Scientific: Caltha palustris
Habitat: Road ditches, stream banks. Common in the lowlands.

Leaves of the marsh-marigold were used in broths early in the spring before it flowered. If you waited until after flowering the leaves were dry and brittle. Some people are said to have squeezed juice from the flowers and mixed it with alum to make yellow ink. People with chest complaints were supposed to breathe in smoke from marsh-marigold and mountains avens leaves or inhale powdered marsh-marigold through the nose.

> "This plant has strange properties because if it is picked in late summer and bathed in lamb's blood and placed next to a wolf's tooth and wrapped in a laurel leaf and worn about one's person, people will only speak kind words to that person. If something is stolen from somebody and one places this plant over the eye, the thief and all his crimes will be revealed."
>
> Jón Árnason, 1961a, Volume 1, p. 644

Marsh-marigold was also known as *kúablóm* in Iceland, or cow flower, probably because it was time to let the cows out when the marsh-marigold began to flower. When the flowers began to lose their petals it was time to start making hay.

HAIRY LADY'S-MANTLE

Icelandic: Hlíðamaríustakkur
Scientific: Alchemilla filicaulis
Habitat: Dells and sheltered places in slopes, grassland, ravines. Common.

Hairy lady's mantle was used in Iceland as a dressing for wounds and was known as a medicinal plant in times past. It was said that the side of the leaf facing the ground could be used to draw out pus, while the upper side could heal wounds. Hairy lady's mantle was used as a yellow dye. It is a plant traditionally associated with women and its Icelandic name is related to the mantle of the Virgin Mary. It is believed to be an effective remedy for complaints specific to women, for example period pains, and as an aid to fertility. If the breasts were washed in a potion made from the plant, the breasts were said to become firmer. The scientific genus name Alchemilla means chemistry and refers to the alchemists who in the past tried to create gold from various materials, including dew drops from lady's mantle. The drops are produced both by transpiration from the plant and from rainfall and were considered effective for rinsing infected eyes.

> *"If one sleeps on a lady's mantle, one will not have nightmares or bad dreams."*

Jón Árnason, 1961a, Volume 1, p. 643

HAREBELL

Icelandic: Bláklukka
Scientific: Campanula rotundifolia
Habitat: Heathland, slopes, grassy meadows and woodland.
Common in the east, rare elsewhere.

Harebell is an abundant flower in eastern Iceland and is unofficially the region's emblematic flower. It has bell-shaped petals and pointed sepals. A blue dye could be produced from the flowers of the harebell by rubbing them into the wool, and if they were boiled they would produce a green colour. It has several other names in English, including lady's thimble and witch's bells.

FIELD GENTIAN

Icelandic: Maríuvöndur
Scientific: Gentianella campestris
Habitat: Dry soil on grassy ground or slopes. Rather common.

Field gentian was an all-round medicinal plant in the past and was used as a remedy for heart complaints, lack of appetite, flatulence, intestinal parasites, cramp, chills and rheumatism. Drops of field gentian root can be made by soaking chopped root in the strongest schnapps for six days and draining the residue.

> "If a field gentian is held in the palm of the hand, it warns the rider
> when the horse is getting tired."
>
> Jónas Jónasson, 1945:409

There are also folk tales about field gentian from graveyards having the power to make people invisible:

> "the flower must be picked during mass and be sprinkled with
> holy water. The field gentian must not be touched with bare hands
> or be exposed to sunlight. The plant should be kept in white silk and
> sacred vestments. When people want to be cloaked with invisibility,
> they should perform the sign of the cross in all four directions,
> raise the field gentian and they will become invisible."
>
> Jón Árnason, 1956, Volume 4, p. 22

COMMON MOONWORT

Icelandic: Tungljurt
Scientific: Botrychium lunaria
Habitat: Grassy hollows and slopes or flat pastures. Common.

Common moonwort was used as an aid to childbirth by placing it next to the woman and then removing it as soon as the baby was born. An old name for the common moonwort was lásagras or "lock grass" as it was thought to be able to open locks if placed next to them. It was said that if a horse stepped on moonwort, it would lose a horseshoe.

NOOTKA LUPIN

Icelandic: Lúpína
Scientific: Lupinus nootkatensis
Habitat: River flats, gravel and hillsides with poor soil. Introduced and cultivated
to fertilize poor soil and reclaim eroded land.

Many parts of Iceland turn blue in June due to the Nootka lupin which was introduced to Iceland at the beginning of the last century as a garden plant and then again in middle of the century to help combat erosion. The lupin has become very widespread and each plant releases around 2100 seeds a year, which can lie dormant in the soil for decades. The lupin is a member of the pea family and forms a symbiotic relationship with rhizobium bacteria which fix nitrogen in the soil and enable other plants to grow. The lupin therefore improves soil fertility and has proven very effective in land reclamation in sandy areas of Iceland. However, it is a highly controversial plant as it spreads very quickly and can create monocultures. The roots of the lupin have medicinal properties and have been used as a herbal remedy by cancer patients in recent decades. The herbal remedy also contains lichen (*Parmelia sp*).

ALPINE GENTIAN

Icelandic: Dýragras
Scientific: Gentiana nivalis
Habitat: Heathland and stubble fields. Common.

Alpine gentian is a common flower across much of Iceland. The head of the flower only opens fully in sunlight or in good light in the middle of the day and it does not take much to make it close again. In Icelandic folklore it was thought to grow in places where the hidden people lived.

MEADOWSWEET

Icelandic: Mjaðjurt
Scientific: Filipendula ulmaria
Habitat: Grassy, moderately moist heathland, meadows, hollows and woodland.
Common in some regions.

Pollen counts have shown that meadowsweet predated Settlement and that it became less common after humans came to Iceland. Written sources from the 18th century mention meadowsweet as a medicinal plant in earlier times.

Ever since Settlement people have drunk an ale made from malt. A travel journal from the 18th century noted that meadowsweet has been used in the past to flavour ale throughout the Nordic region, particularly in Iceland. It was the fragrant flowers which produced the taste.

Meadowsweet contains large quantities of salicylic acid which makes it a good plant for making dye with. It was used as a dye in many areas of Iceland and could produce a yellow colour and black if mixed with mud, as with bearberry. Meadowsweet was also used to tan leather and people sometimes used it instead of birch bark.

> "Meadowsweet can be used to reveal the identity of a thief. It should be picked on Midsummer's Eve and placed in a bowl of clean water. If it floats, the thief is a woman, if it sinks it is a man. The shadow reveals who that person is. You should then say "Thief, I command you to bring home that which you stole from me as God commanded the Devil to leave Paradise for Hell."
>
> Jón Árnason, 1961a, Volume 1, p. 644

Heath Spotted Orchid

Northern Green Orchid:

ORCHID FAMILY
ORCHIDACEAE

Northern Green Orchid: *Friggjargras, Platanthera hyperborea, common.*
Small White Orchid: *Hjónagras, Pseudorchis straminea, Rather common.*
Frog Orchid: *Barnarót, Coeloglossum viride,*
More common in the mountains than in the lowlands.
Coralroot Orchid: *Kræklurót, Corallorhiza trifida, Widespread, never in large quantities.*
Lesser Twayblade: *Hjartatvíblaðka, Listera cordata, Fairly widespread.*
Common Twayblade: *Eggtvíblaðka, Listera ovata, Rare.*
Heath Spotted Orchid: *Brönugrös, Dactylorhiza maculata,*
Frequent in some regions, rare or absent in others.

Seven species of orchid occur in Iceland: northern green orchid, small white orchid heath spotted orchid, common twayblade, lesser twayblade, coralroot orchid and frog orchid. This section will discuss orchids in general without distinguishing between species. The Greek name orchis means testicle because of the shape of the tubers of some species. According to an old folk belief thicker tubers could be used as an aphrodisiac and to enhance pleasure, help alleviate sorrow, increase joy and generally reinvigorate people. Narrower tubers could be given to people to encourage chastity. The Icelandic names of several orchids are associated with love and fertility. Northern green orchid is called *friggjargras* in Icelandic, or Freyja's grass. Freyja was the wife Odin, and was the goddess of love and fertility, and the use of orchids as an aphrodisiac is connected to this. The Icelandic phrase *að ganga á eftir einhverjum með grasið í skónum* or "to beg someone to do something with grass in your shoes" comes from the belief that orchids could be placed in the shoes to stir amorous feelings. Orchids were also slipped under the pillows of the object of desire to make them fall in love. A potion made from the plant was made for the same purpose. In Icelandic there were many traditional names which refer to orchids' supposed links to love, such as lovers' grass, horny root, friends' grass and estrus grass, the latter because it was thought to encourage cattle and other livestock to mate.

In an 18th century textbook on using plants, orchids were said to enhance both male and female fertility. The root stimulated desire, protect the foetus and ensured the baby was born at the right time. The plant's inflorescence, boiled in alcohol, could help regulate the menstrual cycle and aid urination. Harder inflorescences could be soaked in a good quality wine for a while and then the wine could be drunk. Other people cooked the inflorescences or ate them raw with milk or even sugar. Orchids could be used to make an ointment to soothe rashes and internally it was a remedy for stomach cramps and diarrhea. Orchids could bring harmony to arguing couples if they slept on it. According to folklore it could be used to arouse passions in other people:

> "If you wish to use this root to arouse passions, the one seeking love should dig carefully around the root, ensuring that no tendril is broken off either root when removed, otherwise it loses its potency. Once this is done, one of the roots is placed under the pillow of the one you love, ensuring that this person knows nothing of this, and the other one you sleep on yourself. It is said this method never fails to make the other person fall in love, if done correctly."

> Jón Árnason, 1961a, Volume 1, p. 644

Small White Orchid

Frog Orchid

SEA MAYWEED

Icelandic: *Baldursbrá*
Scientific: *Tripleurospermum maritimum subsp. phaeocephalum*
Habitat: *Dumps, waste grounds and industrial fields, also along the coast.*
Common in towns and villages.

An old Icelandic name for sea mayweed is *móðurjurt* or "mother's herb" which indicates that it was used as a treatment for gynecological conditions. If it was boiled in alcohol it was said to be able to treat the after-effects of childbirth. In order to treat period pains, one was supposed to boil crushed sea mayweed in a linen bag and place the bag against the abdomen.

To assist with childbirth, sea mayweed was supposed to be boiled in alcohol and given to the expectant mother. Sea mayweed was also said to be able to tell whether a girl was a virgin or not. If the flower was slipped under the seat of a chair, the girl would not be able to stand up again if she was not a virgin. If someone slept on sea mayweed they would dream about the person who had stolen from them, and dried sea mayweed would drive fleas out of a house.

LYME-GRASS

Icelandic: Melgresi
Scientific: Leymus arenarius
Habitat: Sand, esp. Drifting sand, sandy lava fields and seashores.

Lyme-grass has been present in Iceland since the last ice age. It has a deep root system which makes it an excellent plant for land reclamation and it thrives in areas where other plants find it difficult to take root, such as sandy wastes. Lyme-grass was used as a cereal crop in some parts of Iceland, such as in Skaftafellssýslur in south-east Iceland, where the grain could be used to make flour. In other parts of Iceland the grain did not mature sufficiently to make flour but the stalks and roots were used. The roots were used for padding for packhorses, mattresses, wash cloths, thread and twine for sewing blood puddings. The stalks were used as underlay in turf roofs as they were more durable and less likely to rot than other materials. Using lyme-grass was important in many areas but people had to be careful as if too much was gathered, the lyme-grass could die and leave the farming communities susceptible to devastation from advancing sand wastelands.

BIBLIOGRAPHY

Abyshev A.Z., Agaev É.M. og Guseinov A.B. (2007). Studies of the chemical composition of birch bark extracts (Cortex betula) from the Betulaceae family. *Pharmaceutical Chemistry Journal,41*(8), 22-26. Retrieved on 28 March 2013 from http://link.springer.com/article/10.1007%2Fs11094-007-0091-5#page-1

Anna Rósa Róbertsdóttir. (2011). *Íslenskar lækningajurtir, notkun þeirra og tínsla.* Reykjavík: Anna Rósa grasalæknir ehf.

Arnbjörg Linda Jóhannsdóttir. (2011). *Íslenskar lækningajurtir.* Reykjavík: Mál og menning.

Arnór Sigurjónsson [ed]. (1966). Búalög: *Verðlag á Íslandi á 12.-19.* Reykjavík: Framleiðsluráð.

Ágúst H. Bjarnason. (1983). *Íslensk flóra með litmyndum.* Reykjavík: Iðunn.

Árni Magnússon og Páll Vídalín. (1943). *Jarðabók – Eyjafjarðarsýsla* Volume 10. Reykjavík: Hið íslenska Fræðafélag í Kaupmannahöfn.

Áslaug Sverrisdóttir (ed.). (1978). Spjallað við Hildi Jónsdóttur. Hugur og hönd. [Year and edition missing], p. 13-15.

Áslaug Sverrisdóttir. (1981). Brot úr sögu litunar. *Hugur og hönd,* 16(1), 40-43.

Bjarni Guðnason (ed.). (1957). *Sýslulýsingar 1744-1749.* Reykjavík: Sögufélag.

Bjarni Pálsson. (1881). Um Íslenzk matvæli. *Tímarit hins íslenzka bókmenntafélags,* 11(1), 64-71.

Björn Halldórsson. (1983). *Rit Björns Halldórssonar í Sauðlauksdal.* Reykjavík: Búnaðarfélag Íslands. (First edition 1783).

Eggert Ólafsson og Bjarni Pálsson. (1943). *Ferðabók Eggerts Ólafssonar og Bjarna Pálssonar, um ferðir þeirra á Íslandi árin 1752-1757.* Reykjavík: Haraldur Sigurðsson og Helgi Hálfdánarson. (First edition 1772).

Eggert Ólafsson. (1774). *Stutt agrip úr Lachanologia eda mat-urta-Bok fyrrum Vice-Lögmannsins Hr. Eggerts Olaf Sonar um Gard-Yrkiu aa Islandi* [Björn Halldórsson sá um útgáfuna]. Kaupmannahöfn: Björn Halldórsson og Magnús Ólafsson.

Finnboga saga ramma. (1985). Í Jón Torfason (ed.), Sverrir Tómasson (ed.) og Örnólfur Thorsson (ed.), *Íslendingasögur* Volume 1. Reykjavík: Svart á Hvítu.

Fóstbræðra saga. (1985). Í Jón Torfason (ed.), Sverrir Tómasson (ed.) og Örnólfur Thorsson (ed.), *Íslendingasögur* Volume 1. Reykjavík: Svart á Hvítu.

Framhaldsskóli.is. (á.á.). Retrieved May 6th 2013 from http://gatt.framhaldsskoli.is/_framhaldsskoli/_valmynd/keilir/pdf/bunadarbalkur_eggert_olafsson.pdf.

Franz Gíslason. (2004). Grasaættin. *Niðjar Þórunnar Gísladóttur og Filippusar Stefánssonar.* Reykjavík: Ritnefnd Grasaættarinnar.

Frisak. (1894). *Norsk farvebog,100 opskrifter til farvning med plantefarver.* Kristiania: Kunstindustrimuseet.

Fægri, K. (1970). *Norges Planter* (2nd edition) Volumes 1 and 2 Oslo: J. W. Cappelens forlag A. S.

Gísli Kristjánsson [bjó til prentunar]. (1979). *Móðir mín húsfreyjan.* Reykjavík: Skuggsjá.

Gísli Oddsson. (1942).*Undur Íslands*. (Translated by Jónas Rafnar) Akureyri: Þorsteinn M. Jónsson. (First edition1817).

Guðbjörg Auður Guðjónsdóttir og Kristín Ingólfsdóttir. (1997). Quantitative determination of protolichesterinic and fumarprotocetraric acids in Cetraria islandica by high performance liquid cromatography. *Journal of chromatography A,757*(1.), 303-306.

Guðmundur Finnbogason (ed.). (1943). *Iðnsaga Íslands* Volume 2. Reykjavík: Iðnaðarmannafélagið í Reykjavík.

Guðmundur Jónsson. (1830). *Safn af íslenzkum orðskviðum, fornmælum, heilræðum, snilliyrðum, sannmælum og málsgreinum.* Kaupmannahöfn: Hið íslenzka bókmennta-félag.

Gunnar Karlsson. (1992). *Í formála að Grágás.* Reykjavík: Mál og menning

Halldóra Bjarnadóttir. (1928). Jurtalitun. *Hlín 12*(1), 58-65.

Halldóra Bjarnadóttir. (1944). Gömul íslensk matargerð. *Hlín, 27*(1),78-93.

Halldóra Bjarnadóttir (1961a). „Ávöxtur, gróði og aldin klár oss verði að nota sjerhvert ár." Frásagnir merkra manna, karla og kvenna, um Landsnytjar: Matföng og læknislyf, úr ríki náttúru Íslands. (Sagnirnar skráðar eftir gömlu fólki fyrir 30-40 árum.). *Hlín, (43)*1, 33-37.

Halldóra Bjarnadóttir. (1973). Hollt er heima hvat. *Garðyrkjuritið, 58*(1) 57-64.

Hallgerður Gísladóttir. (1999). *Íslensk matarhefð.* Reykjavík: Mál og menning.

Hannes Finnsson. (1970). *Mannfækkun af hallærum.* Reykjavík: Almenna bókafélagið. (First edition 1796).

Helga Sigurðardóttir. (2009). *Matur og drykkur.* Reykjavík: Bókaútgáfan Opna.

Helgi Hallgrímsson. (1962). *Um hvannir og hvannaneyzlu.* Ársrit Ræktunarfélags Norðurlands 59(1), 97-107.

Heslop-Harrison,Y. (2004). *Pinguicula L. Journal of Ecology. 92*,1071-1118.

Hooker,W. J. (2000). *Ferð um Ísland 1809.* (Translated and published by Arngrímur Thorlacius). Reykjavík: Fósturmold. (First edition1811)

Horrebow, N. (1966). *Frásagnir um Ísland* (Translated by Steindór Steindórsson). Reykjavík: Bókfellsútgáfan hf. (First edition1758).

Høeg, O.A. (1976). *Planter og tradisjon, Floraen i levende tale og tradisjon i Norge 1925-1973.* Oslo, Bergen,Tromsö: Universitetsforlaget.

Hörður Kristinsson. (1968). Fléttunytjar. *Flóra, 6.*(1), 19-25.

Hörður Kristinsson. (1997). *Nýgræðingar í flórunni, innfluttar plöntur – saga, áhrif, framtíð,*[Ráðstefnurit]. Bls.6-9. Reykjavík: Félag garðyrkjumanna.

Hörður Kristinsson. (2010). *Íslenska plöntuhandbókin. Blómplöntur og byrkningar.* Reykjavík: Mál og menning.

Ingólfur Davíðsson. (1965b 4. júlí). Mörgum var hvönnin mikið í huga. *Tíminn,* p. 578 og 598.

Ingólfur Davíðsson. (1974). *Blómin okkar.* Reykjavík: Ríkisútgáfa námsbóka.

Ingólfur Davíðsson. (1978, 5. nóvember). Sumarið hvatt, vetri heilsað. *Tíminn,* p. 34-35.

Ingólfur Davíðsson. (1986). Fróðleiksmolar úr gróðurríkinu. Hugur og hönd.[Árgang og tölublað vantar], p.40-41.

Ingólfur Guðnason. (2004). Jurtagarður í Skálholti. Skálholt: Skálholtsskóli.

Johnsen, B. (1932). Lyfjagrasið. Náttúrufræðingurinn, 2(7-8), 117-119.

Jóhann Ólafur Halldórsson. (1988, miðvikudagur, 15. júní). Sækist eftir ætinjóla á hverju sumri: „Eins og hvert annað hollt grænmeti"- segir Mývetningurinn Illugi Jónsson. Dagur, p. 13.

Jón Aðalsteinn Jónsson og Svavar Sigmundsson [sáu um útgáfuna]. (1997). Skaftafellssýsla. Sýslu- og sóknalýsingar, Hins íslenska bókmenntafélags 1839-1873. Reykjavík: Sögufélag.

Jón Árnason. (1956). Íslenzkar þjóðsögur og ævintýri Volume 4, (New collection). Reykjavík: Bókaútgáfan þjóðsaga. (First edition 1862-1864).

Jón Árnason. (1958). Íslenzkar þjóðsögur og ævintýri Volume 5, (New collection). Reykjavík: Bókaútgáfan þjóðsaga. (First edition 1862-1864).

Jón Árnason. (1961a). Íslenzkar þjóðsögur og ævintýri Volume 1, (New edition). Reykjavík: Bókaútgáfan þjóðsaga. (First edition 1862-1864).

Jónas Jónasson. (1945). Íslenzkir þjóðhættir,(2nd edition). Reykjavík: Jónas og Halldór Rafnar.

Kristín Þorsteinsdóttir. (1942). Jurtalitun forsagnir. Reykjavík: Skrifstofan íslensk ull.

Kristleifur Þorsteinsson. (1960). Úr byggðum Borgarfjarðar Volume 3. Reykjavík: Ísafoldarprentsmiðja.

Kristleifur Þorsteinsson. (1971). Úr byggðum Borgarfjarðar Volume 1, (2nd edition). Reykjavík: [No publisher].

Kristleifur Þorsteinsson. (1972). Úr byggðum Borgarfjarðar Volume 2, (2nd edition). Reykjavík: [No publisher].

Lakshmi, T., Geetha, R. V., Anitha Roy og Aravind Kumar, S. (2011). Yarrow (Achillea millefolium Linn) A herbal medicinal plant with broad therapeutic use – A review. International Journal of Pharmaceutical Sciences Review & Research 9(2), 126-141. Retrieved on 3 January 2013 from http://globalresearchonline.net/journalcontents/volume9issue2/Article-022.pdf

Lögbók Magnúsar konungs, Lagabætis, handa Íslendingum, eður Jónsbók hin forna; lögtekin á alþingi 1281, (1858). Akureyri: Sveinn Skúlason.

M. K. Jónsdóttir [Fornöfn vantar]. (1926). Berin. Hlín 10(1), 63-65.

Mairet, E. M. (1938). Vegetable dyes, Being a book of Recipies and other information useful to the Dyer. London: Faber and Faber ltd. (First edition 1916).

Margrét Bragadóttir. (2003). Áhrif þörunga og lækningajurta á geymsluþol loðnulýsis. Rannsóknastofnun fiskiðnaðarins. Retrieved on 14 December 2014 from website of Matís: http://www.matis.is/media/frettir/Skyrsla-29-03.pdf tekið 14.

Margrét Hallsdóttir. (1999). Birch pollen abundance in Reykjavik, Iceland. Grana 38(6), 368–373.

Margrjet Jónsdóttir [Svo skráð]. (1928). Öl af íslenskum grösum. Hlín, 12(1), 26-28.

Matthildur Halldórsdóttir. (1944). Um jurtalitun. Reykjavík: [No publisher].

Mohr, N. (1786). Forsøg til en Islandsk Naturhistorie : med adskillige oekonomiske samt andre Anmærkninger. Kaupmannahöfn: [No publisher].

Oddur Jónsson Hjaltalín. (1930). *Íslenzk grasafræði*. Kaupmannahöfn: Hið íslenzka bókmenntafélag.

Ólafur Olavíus. (1964). *Ferðabók*.

Landshagir í norðvestur-, norður- og norðaustursýslum Íslands 1775-1777, ásamt ritgerðum Ole Henckels um brennistein og brennisteinsnám og Christian Zieners um surtarbrand. Reykjavík: Bókfellsútgáfan. (First edition 1780).

Park, S.Y., Lee, E. S., Han, S. H., Lee, H.Y. and Lee, S. (2011). Antioxidative effects of two native berry species, Empetrum nigrum var. Japonicum K. Koch and Rubus buergeri Miq., from the Jeju island of Korea. *Journal of Food Biochemistry*, 36(6): 675–682. Retrieved on 13 January 2012 from http://onlinelibrary.wiley.com/doi/10.1111/j.1745-4514.2011.00582.x/full.

Schübeler, F.C. (1873). *Die Pflanzenwelt Norwegens 1875*. Kristiania: Veranlassung des academischen Collegiums als Universitäta-Program.

Sigrún Helgadóttir og Þorgerður Hlöðversdóttir. (2010). *Foldarskart í ull og fat. Jurtalitun*. Reykjavík: Sigrún Helgadóttir og Þorgerður Hlöðversdóttir.

Stefán Sigfússon. (1893). Um hina helztu sjúkdóma og kvilla búpenings vors. *Búnaðarritið*, 7(1), 123-168.

Steindór Steindórsson. (1978). *Íslensk plöntunöfn*. Reykjavík: Bókaútgáfa Menningarsjóðs.

Sturla Friðriksson. (1954). Hinn heilagi eldur. *Náttúrufræðingurinn*. 24(4), 161-176.

Sveinn Pálsson. (1945). *Ferðabók Sveins Pálssonar, Dagbækur og ritgerðir 1791-1797*. Reykjavík: [No publisher].

Sveinn Runólfsson. (1988). Íslenska melgresið. Í Andrés Arnalds (ed.), *Græðum Ísland, Landgræðslan 1907-1987* (p. 131-155). Gunnarsholt: Landgræðslan.

Sæmundur Magnússon Hólm. (1958). Um meltakið í vesturparti Skaftafellssýslu. Í Arnór Sigurjónsson (ed.), *Sandgræðslan 50 ára*, (p.102-139). Reykjavík: Búnaðarfélag Íslands og Sandgræðsla ríkisins.

Tómas Einarsson (ed.) og Helgi Magnússon (ed.). (1989). *Íslandshandbókin 1*-Volume 2. Reykjavík: Örn og Örlygur.

Troil (1961). *Bréf frá Íslandi* (Translated by Haraldur Sigurðsson). Reykjavík: Menningarsjóður.

Um drykkjurtir. (1885, 14. mars). *Norðanfari*, p. 39.

Underretning og den Islandske moss eller Fieldegræs. (1782). Þrándheimi: [No publisher].

Þorleifur Einarsson. (1962). Vitnisburður frjógreiningar um gróðurfar, veðurfar og landnám á Íslandi. *Saga 3*(3), 442-469.

Þorvaldur Thoroddsen. (1919). *Lýsing Íslands* Volume 3. Kaupmannahöfn: Hið íslenszka Bókmenntafélag.

Þorvaldur Thoroddsen. (1922). *Lýsing Íslands* Volume 4. Kaupmannahöfn: Hið íslenzka Bókmenntafélag.

Þórdís Stefánsdóttir. (1919). *Jurtalitir*. Reykjavík: Heimilisiðnaðarfélag Íslands.

Þórður Tómasson. (1988). *Þjóðhættir og þjóðtrú*. Reykjavík: Örn og Örlygur.